THE NIGHTMARES OF
DREAM TOPPING

Born in 1948, Merrily Harpur went to Headington School, Oxford and Trinity College, Dublin, where she read English. Realizing she had to live on her wits, she became a cartoonist. Her cartoons are published regularly in Punch and the Guardian and have appeared in The Times (for whom she also writes), Financial Times, Daily Express, Radio Times and Euromoney.

Merrily has illustrated a number of books, including the best-selling series of Franglais books by Miles Kington and Jill Tweedie's Letters From a Fainthearted Feminist. She has also compiled and illustrated a selection of letters to The Field, published by Robson Books under the title of Pig Overboard!

THE NIGHTMARES OF DREAM TOPPING

BY MERRILY HARPUR

Robson Books

The author would like to thank the proprietors of *Punch* magazine for permission to reproduce material in this book.

FIRST PUBLISHED IN GREAT BRITAIN IN 1984
BY ROBSON BOOKS LTD., BOLSOVER HOUSE,
5-6 CLIPSTONE STREET, LONDON W1P 7EB.
COPYRIGHT © 1984 PUNCH PUBLICATIONS

British Library Cataloguing in Publication Data
The nightmares of dream topping.
1. English wit and humor, Pictorial
I. Harpur, Merrily II. Punch
741.5'942   NC1479

ISBN 0-86051-302-5

Printed in Hungary

THE NIGHTMARES ARE GARDENING:

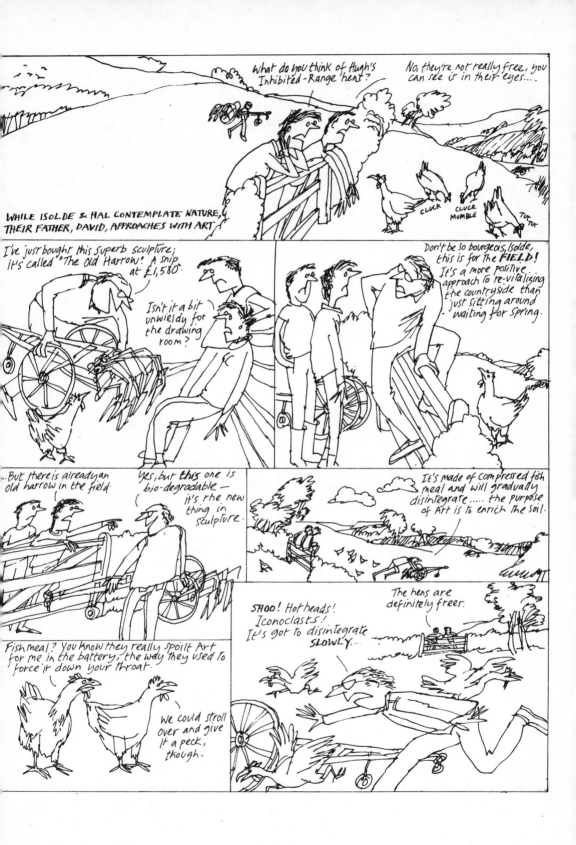

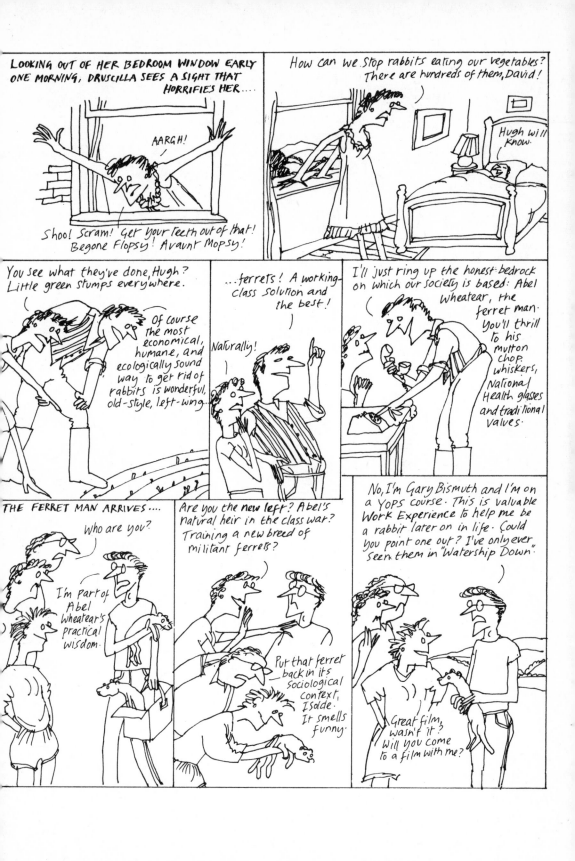

Where is one's little trug?

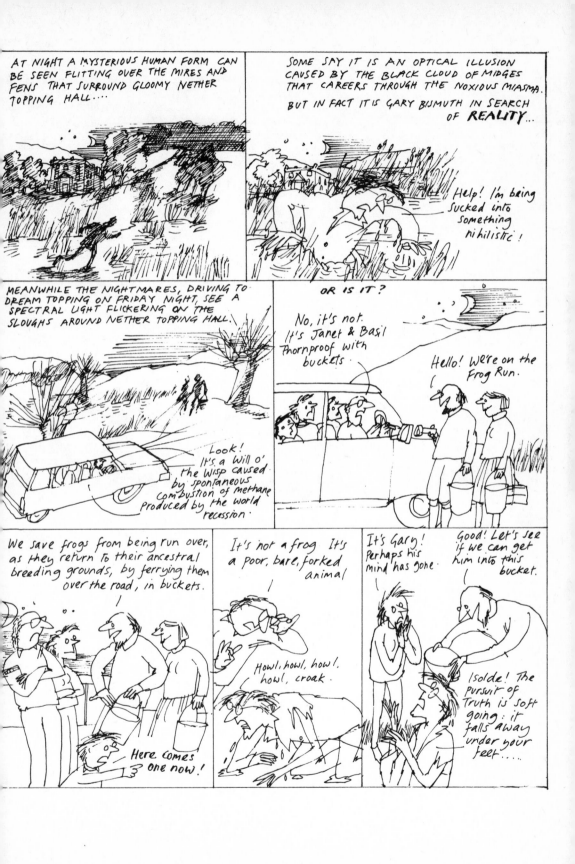

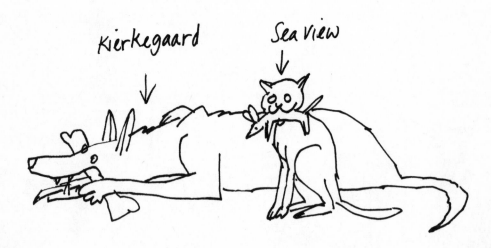